Jumbo Coloring & Activity Book

This is **VAMPIRINA HAUNTLEY**.
Her family calls her Vee. You can, too!

Written by Sheila Higginson

Illustrated by the Imaginism Studio
and the Disney Storybook Art Team

Ashland, OH 44805
www.bendonpub.com

Boris and Oxana are Vee's dad and mom.
They are very proud of their little girl!

The Hauntleys are a
little **DIFFERENT** from most families.

Can you guess why?
Connect the dots to see what makes them special.

4

VEE IS A VAMPIRE!

She lives in Transylvania.
She has lots of **COOL** monster friends there.

She has other friends, too.
Demi is the **GHOST** who haunts Vee's house.

Chef Remy is the family chef who cooks
the **SPOOKIEST** meals in Transylvania!

Wolfie is the family pet.

Boris and Oxana have a surprise for Vee.
Use the code to find out what the message says.

_ _ _ _ _ _ _ _ _ _ _ _

© Disney

The Hauntleys are **MOVING** to Pennsylvania!

They're going to live in their Great Uncle Dieter's house.

HELLO, PENNSYLVANIA!

"It sure looks **SPOOKY** in here," Vee says.
"It feels like home!"

There are 6 differences between the two pictures of Vee's new bedroom. Can you find them?

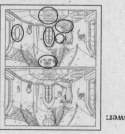

Answer:

Vee and Demi play vampire tag in the new house.
"No fair disappearing through things!" Vee shouts.

Vee meets Gregoria, the **GRUMPY** gargoyle.
She's lived in the house for hundreds of years!

"I can't wait to make more new friends," Vee cheers.
"Just remember love," Boris says. "Humans are a little jumpy."

EEEKS! The doorbell starts to shriek.
The first visitor has arrived!

"WELCOME TO THE NEIGHBORHOOD!"

says Edna Peepleson.

She gives Oxana a bouquet of flowers.

Look down and across to find the flower names listed below.

```
X V P O P P Y U G Q
L I R N S E Z T M A
I O O B P T A H T W
L L S L A U G X J D
A E E U N P C O A
C T X E S I J U C I
E Y Y B Y A N F I S
X Y W E A T Y M X Y
A L I L Y D A B X M
O T U L I P Z N W E
```

DAISY   **BLUEBELL**

ROSE   **LILY**

PETUNIA   **VIOLET**

TULIP   **POPPY**

PANSY   **LILAC**

Answer:

20

© Disney

Edna meets Penelope the man-eating plant.
"AAHHHHH!!!" she screams.

"You're right, Dad," Vee says. "Humans are jumpy."

"What if I don't make any friends
in Pennsylvania?" she worries.

"Let's show the whole human world
how lovable you are!" Demi says.

Which picture of Vee and Demi is different?

A

B

C

D

24

"Hi! I'm Poppy," the girl next door says.
"This is my brother Edgar."

"And I'm Bridget!" another girls says.

"I'm Vampirina," says Vee. "I just moved in."

"Edgar thinks your house is **HAUNTED**," Poppy admits.

Help Vee lead Poppy and Edgar to her house.

Answer:

"Hello new friends!" Boris and Oxana cheer,
surprising Poppy and Edgar.

"WELCOME!"

0

Vee and Poppy race to Vee's room to play.

"MEET THE SCREAM GIRL DOLLS!"
Franken-Stacey, Ghastly Gayle and Creepy Caroline.

Can you find 10 bats hidden in this picture?

Answer:

"HUMAN!"

Demi shouts when he sees Poppy.

"GHOST!"

Poppy shouts when she sees Demi.

At the end of each row, circle the correct picture to finish the pattern.

Answer:

"It's just me, Vampirina," Vee says.

"AH HA!" Edgar says. "I knew something
strange was going on in here!"

"I screamed because we both
love Justin Teether!" Poppy says.

"I wanted to be your friend before you
turned into a bat," Poppy tells Vee.

"Why wouldn't I want to be
your friend afterwards, too?"

Unscramble the letters to read Vee's invitation.

OEMC

_ _ _ _

ESPEL

_ _ _ _ _

VREO

_ _ _ _

TA

_ _

YM

_ _

UOHES

_ _ _ _ _

Vee wants everything to look normal.
Human normal!

"You're going to have to stay hidden," Vee tells Demi.

© Disney

"OH MY GOSH!" Bridget says when she sees Wolfie.
"He's so cute!"

Wolfie is not so cute during a full moon, though!

Boris needs to find Wolfie's crate.
Circle it for him.

Answer:

Poppy and Bridget want to play hide and seek.

"LOOK OUT!" Oxana calls.
"A SPIDER!" Bridget screams.

LOOK OUT,
WEREWOLF!

Bridget runs into someone even scarier!

Vee has an idea. Boris' sunlamp does the trick.
Wolfie is back to his dog form!

Now she just has to find her friends.
Help Vee get to Poppy and Bridget.

Answer:

"I'm afraid your friends may have seen some of our things from Transylvania," Oxana says.

It's time for Vee to show her friends that her house—and her family—are different.

"Wait, they're kind of cute!" Bridget says.

Find and circle all the pictures of Demi.
How many can you find?

Answer:

57

It's time for a pillow fight!

Find and circle the 4 items that the girls will use to sleep.

Answer:

Bridget snuggles up to a Scream Girl doll.

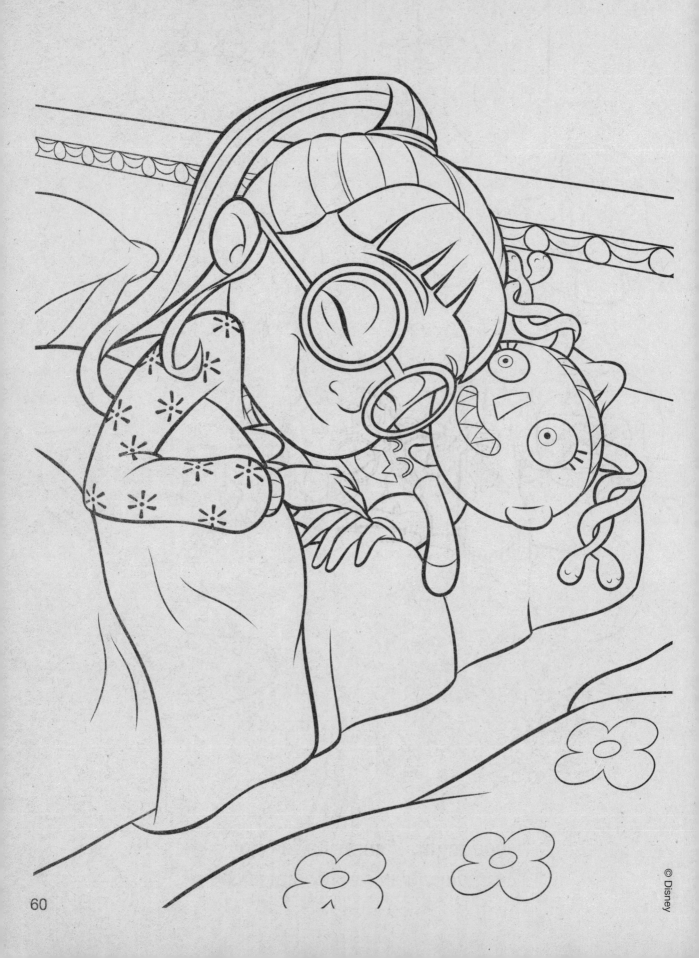

"Good night, Vampirina!" Poppy says.
"Your sleepover was a total success!"

Vampirina still has to get used
to the sleeping at night thing.

But there's one thing she doesn't have
to get used to anymore…

...her home in

PENNSYLVANIA!